Fairy Tale
Phonics

Brown Watson
ENGLAND

Contents

Let's have some fun with phonics!

These classic fairy tales have been retold with a twist, to help your children recognise and practise key sounds that they will be learning at school. Each story has a vowel sound highlighted in red, and a secondary consonant sound picked out in blue.
Read the stories together and point out the sounds in coloured text. Repeat them out loud and listen closely. Look at the different ways the key sounds can be used – for example, the 'l' sound in old, lady and will. Have fun thinking of other words that use the same sounds, and combine them to sound out new words.

Take it slowly, and stop when your child has had enough. You can still enjoy the stories and their colourful illustrations without focusing on the phonics. Soon your child will have discovered some timeless tales, and learned reading skills as they go.
Enjoy your time together!

Snow White

Once upon a time, a King and his wife had a baby girl. She had skin as white as snow, and hair as black as midnight. But the poor Queen died and the King took a new bride.

She took great delight in talking to her magic mirror. 'You are the one they all admire,' it advised. But one night, the mirror gave a different reply.

'Snow White is the finest in this land!'
the mirror chimed. 'That can't be right!'
the stepmother cried. 'She must die!'

Snow White ran away to hide. She found a little cottage and went inside. The dwarfs who lived there got quite a fright when they found her lying in their bed!

'Would you like to live with us?' they asked shyly. 'That's a fine idea! You're very kind,' Snow White replied.

The stepmother disguised herself. She gave Snow White a shiny red apple to try. When the girl took a bite the stepmother gave an evil smile. It had poison inside!

The dwarfs all cried. 'She might be alive,' they whispered, and laid her in a glass coffin outside.

A Prince rode by and saw Snow White. He kissed her ruby lips and she opened her eyes. 'She's alright!' the dwarfs sighed. 'She didn't die!'

Hansel and Gretel

Hansel and Gretel were often hungry. Their father had no job and their stepmother was always cross. 'We do not have enough food!'

'Follow me,' said their father sadly, and he led them into the forest. 'Sit here on this log while I collect food and firewood.'

The children cried when they realised their father was not coming back. 'We are lost in the woods,' they sobbed.

They found a little cottage and knocked on the door. 'It is made of chocolate!' they gasped. A blind old lady took them inside.

The old lady was a witch, and she locked Hansel in a cage. 'I will fatten you up to eat you!' she cackled. She made Gretel mop the floor, and cook lots of food.

Every day the witch prodded Hansel
to see if he got any fatter. Hansel
pretended that a stick was his bony
finger. 'You are not fat enough yet!'
she said crossly.

Then one day, she stopped feeding him.
'Make that fire nice and hot!' the witch
called. 'I will cook you in a pot!'

The witch unlocked the cage and Hansel hopped out. He pushed the witch in there instead. The children ran off to find their father.

The Ugly Duckling

Mummy duck sat on her nest. She had six blue eggs and one big brown one. They would soon hatch into ducklings.

'Look at you!' she cooed when her babies hatched. She led them to the pool to teach them to swim.

All the ducklings were yellow except for one ugly grey one. His cruel brothers teased him until he ran away to a farm.

The birds in the farmyard were mean, too. The rooster pecked him and the goose kicked him. The hens ate all his food.

Snow came and the cold winds blew. The pond was frozen. A kind man carried him home and cared for him through the winter.

The wife didn't like the duckling. 'We have no room for you to live here!' she cried. 'Shoo!' He flew far away.

He landed by a pool where two swans with smooth white feathers were swimming. 'Who are you?' they asked.

'Just an ugly duckling,' he replied.
'That's not true,' said the swans. The
duckling saw his reflection in the pool.
He had grown up and turned into
a swan, too!

Key Sounds

Say these words out loud. Which story are they from?
Listen for the sounds you have learned.

children   **lost**

blind   **locked**

little

birds   **hatched**

food   **pond**

pecked